RIDDLES FOR KIDS

AGE 9-15

200 Funny and Stimulating Riddles, Trick Questions
and Creating Brain Teasers to Entertain Smart Kids
and the Whole Family Vol 2.

Table Of Contents

INTRODUCTION

All kids love jokes, all of them love to have a good laugh from hearing, reading or telling jokes and that is why I have painstakingly compiled over 200 educative and fun filled jokes and riddles for their pleasure. Apart from the fact that jokes are for laughs and fun, both jokes and riddles have a lot of other importance to the intellectual growth of kids and how they socialize.

Jokes help them socialize better in school and home with both their classmates and family members, it also helps them get over the stress of the day. The riddles are amazing at helping kids develops critical thinking and problem solving skills which will even help them in their classwork and everyday activities as they grow older. Riddles and jokes also has a way of improving the comprehension skills of your kids, a lot of people can read but cannot understand or comprehend but reading and listening to joke that arc intellectual and good for the brain helps your kid develop their comprehension skills from a very young age. Riddles and Jokes can also help your kids build their confidence because they always feel like they have something to offer and they are not afraid to step out in front of their classmates and make speeches or have an intellectual conversation with whoever as they also help them improve their vocabulary to an enviable extent.

Most importantly, riddles and jokes are good bonding links for parents and kids and if properly explored, it can help build up unforgettable memories that everyone can look back to and smile when your kids grow older.

Finally, riddles will help your kids see things from different perspective as they get to realize things are not always 'direct' and they will all get to live life more happily as they enjoy their childhood.

The riddles in the book are non-provocative, contains absolutely no adult content, are witty, educative and intellectual. They range from animals joke, to knock knock, to sport, to education to food and so on. If you want to build a stronger bond with your kids while they live a happy life too, I recommend you to get this book.

COMPILATION OF INTELLIGENT AND FUNNY RIDDLES AND JOKES FOR KIDS.

BEGINNER LEVEL

Riddles and jokes ranges from beginner level to pro level making it very versatile brain teaser for kids and adults. Here are some riddles that are more appropriate for kids and adults that just new to this niche.

1. CAN February March?

2. What would a flower say after saying a joke?

3. A Koala went for a job interview, performed well but still didn't get the job, why?

4. Where is the favourite sleeping place of rocks?

5. No matter how big this room gets, you can't enter, what room is it?

6. What you do call a deer without eyes?

7. What did the monitor say to the keyboard?

8. What did the English textbook say to the maths textbook?

9. What vehicle takes squids to school?

10. What word has t in it, starts and ends with t?

11. How do the customer care agents answer phone calls at the paint store?

12. How do make a bull not to charge?

13. How do cats bake their cakes?

14. It took 50 workers three months and two days to build a bridge, how long will I take 25 workers to build the same bridge?

15. There is a kid in the playground having fun at the moment, what is her name?

16. Where do squirrels go when they have tooth related problems?

17. Why did the maths textbook look so sad?

18. It has functioning hands but can't carry anything?

19. What do you call a flower that requires electricity to function?

20. When cattle want to make orders, what do they go through?

21. How do you tell that a farmer is good at what he does?

22. What do you call the horse of the man that lives next door?

23. What did one ocean say to the other?

24. knock-knock. Who is there? Leaf. Leaf who?

25. Where do wasps go when they are ill?

26. Where do baby cows no eat?

27. Why did the pig enter the kitchen?

28. Knock-knock. Who is there? Duane. Duane who?

29. How do you keep someone in suspense?

30. Knock-knock. Who is there? I am outstanding? Outstanding who?

31. What did a plate say to the other?

32. What do you call a bear with no shoes on?

33. What kind of parasite lives in books?

34. Why did the melon jump into the river?

35. What did the egg at the top of the crate say to the one below?

36. It is a nut but has no shell, what nut is it?

37. What did the volcano say to its lover?

38. How do you determine that a moon has eaten enough?

39. What kind of witch likes going to the beach?

40. How do trees get on the internet?

41. It has three letters and starts with gas, what is it?

42. What do kids engage in when they can't play with their phones?

43. Why was the weightlifter angry?

44. What events do spiders love to attend the most?

45. It hard to tell a joke around glass, why?

46. Why is it unpleasant to tell jokes about pizzas?

47. What time is it when someone is throwing stones towards your head?

48. Why didn't the lamp sink?

49. Where do you find a cow with no legs?

50. Why is it hard to trust zoo-keepers with anything?

RIDDLE SOLUTIONS

BEGINNER LEVEL SOLUTIONS

1. no. but April May.

2. I was just pollen (pulling) your legs.

3. Because it was over-koala-fied.

4. Bedrock.

5. Mushroom.

6. No eye-dear (idea).

7. You are my type.

8. Wow, you've got so many problems.

9. Octobus.

10. Teapot.

11. Yellow.

12. You unplug it.

13. From the scratch.

14. None. The bridge is already built.

15. What.

16. To the rodentist.

17. Because it had a lot of problems.

18. A clock.

19. A Powerplant.

20. The cattle-logs.

21. When he is out-standing in his field.

22. Neighbor.

23. Nothing. They just wav

24. Leaf me alone.

25. Waspital.

26. Calf-etaria.

27. He felt like baking.

28. Duane the tub, I am about to

drown.

29. I will let you know next week.

30. I am out-standing in the rain,

please open up and let me in.

31. Lunch is on me.

32. Bare feet.

33. Bookworms.

34. So it could become a watermelon.

35. You crack me up.

36. A doughnut.

37. I lava you so much.

38. When it is full.

39. Sandwitch.

40. They log in.

41. A car.

42. Bored games.

43. He worked with dumbbells.

44. Webinars.

45. It could crack up.

46. Because they are too cheesy.

47. Time to duck.

48. Because it was too light.

49. Exactly where you left him.

50. They like cheetahs.

INTERMEDIATE LEVEL

Welcome to the Intermediate level of your favourites riddles and jokes. How many did you get right on the beginner level? Let proceed with the second part

1. What is a bear with no ear called?

2. Why did the shark burst into laughter?

3. Where do popular dragons retire to when they are done?

4. Where should you take your pet pig for fun?

5. Say the word 'milk' ten times, no what do cows drink?

6. What did the worker bee said when he returned to the hive?

7. What does sharks love eating the most?

8. What animal always sleeps with shoes on?

9. What do you call a fish that does not like sharing with others?

10. What can't cheetahs engage in the hide and seek game?

11. Why do Gorillas have big fingers?

12. How do you catch a rabbit?

13. What name do you call an angry polar bear?

14. What do you call a snail that is in a ship?

15. What is the main difference between a flea and a dog?

16. What is the main difference between a fly and a bird?

17. What kind of musical instruments would mouse play?

18. How else can you catch a school of fish?

19. How better can you communicate with a fish?

20. What kind of animals belongs to clock?

21. What happens when you throw butter?

22. Let's say a rooster laid a brown egg first, then laid a white

egg later, what kind of chick would such rooster hatch.

23. It is hard to crack jokes with snakes, why?

24. What name do you call an Italian cow that loves taking coffee?

25. It is a mousetrap but has only three letters, what is it?

26. Where are horses referred to when they are ill?

27. Why did the leopard refuse to have a shower?

28. What had the small ant confused?

29. What animal should one not play video games with?

30. Why would you take a base player to the camp?

31. Why is a car not allowed to play football?

32. If you have an umpire in tennis, a referee in boxing and football, what do you have in bowls?

33. Why would the coach go to the bank?

34. What insect is cowardly in nature?

35. Why was the finish without money?

36. What kind of air is the richest?

37. Where do you check whenever you always want to find happiness?

38. Why did the orange lose the race?

39. What do you call a dark coloured horse that is very scary?

40. What is totally yours but your friends use more often than you do?

41. What actually happens when you throw a blue rock into a yellow river?

42. What kind of house weighs the least?

43. What has no arms but has hands?

44. How do you attach a wall to the tree?

45. Did you hear about the man that got his left arm chopped off?

46. What do you normally take before any meal?

47. Which nail does the carpenter loves not to hit at all?

48. What happens every-time when computer geeks meet?

49. What would be a dentist favourite game?

50. What ten letter would start with gas?

INTERMEDIATE LEVEL SOLUTIONS

1. B.

2. Because it saw the bottom of the sea.

3. Hall of flame.

4. HAM-usement park.

5. Water.

6. Honey, I am back.

7. Fish and ships.

8. Horse.

). Shellfish (selfish).

10. Because he is already been spotted.

11. Because they have large nostrils.

12. Dress up like are a carrot.

13. Nothing, but run!

14. A snailor.

15. A dog can have fleas but a fleas definitely can't have dogs.

16. A bird can fly but a fly can't

bird.

17. Mouse organs.

18. By using a bookworm.

19. Drop it a line.

20. Ticks.

21. butter-flies.

22. None. Roosters are not egg

layers.

23. Because you can't pull it's legs.

24. A de-calf.

25. Cat.

26. Horse-pitals.

27. He did not want to lose it's spots.

28. Because all his uncles were ants (aunts).

29. Cheetahs.

30. So he can help pitch the tent.

31. Because it has just one booth.

32. Goldfish.

33. Just to his quarter-back.

34. A flea.

35. He left them all at the riverbank.

36. A billionAIRe

37. The dictionary.

38. Because he ran out of juice.

39. A nightMARE.

40. Your name.

41. It will produce a splash.

42. The LIGHThouse.

43. A clock.

44. with the duck tape.

45. He is all-right now.

46. A meal.

47. The thumbnail.

48. It is always love at first site.

49. Tooth or dare.

50. A M-O-T-O-R-C-Y-C-L-E.

PRO LEVEL

Welcome to the pro level of your favourites riddles and jokes. How many did you get right on the intermediate level? Let proceed with the pro level.

1. What animal always need to wear a wig?

2. Why was the toilet paper unable to cross the road to the other side?

3. What would bears be without a bee?

4. What disappears every time you stand up?

5. The kind of running that involves walking is?

6. Why would a policeman stay in bed all day?

7. There are four letters that scares thieves and sends shiver

down their spine when they hear it, what are they?

8. If a man was born in England, raised in France and died in Iran, what is he?

9. What happen when you throw a green stone into a red sea?

10. If you are participating in a race and you just passed the guy that was in third place, what place are you?

11. What normally runs around a house but never leaves a place?

12. How many sides do circles normally have?

13. What kind of animals did Moses included in the ark and what was their total number?

14. What do computer geeks have as snacks the most?

15. What normally becomes smaller the moment you turn it upside down?

16. It makes songs but never sings, what is it?

17. What has just two back bones but thousands of ribs?

18. What can one call a superhero that just lost all its powers?

19. Why do you think the doctor is angry?

20. How do you put a lion in the refrigerator?

21. How do you put a crocodile in the refrigerator?

22. There a meeting that the animals attended in the jungle, one of them was absent, who was it and why?

23. A man was passing by in the jungle and there was a stream in his way and he was scared to cross because wild animals

normally reside in the stream, nevertheless, he crossed safely, how?

24. Imagine you were in a car and you needed to alight but the break won't work, how do you get out?

25. It is black when clean but white when dirty, what is it?

26. Which of hot and cold is faster?

27. The higher it gets, the smaller it becomes, it lower it gets, the bigger it becomes, what is it?

28. The calculator is always sad because?

29. What would a dragon say after laying four dozens of eggs?

30. Three were four men in a boat, the boat capsized but only three men had their hair wet, how is that possible?

31. What kind of tea is very hard to drink?

32. Who do you think is the most beautiful in the whole world?

33. The more you take of it, the more you leave behind, what are they?

34. Why did the boy took a ruler to bed yesterday?

35. How many second are in a month?

36. What did delaware?

37. What are soldiers favourite month?

38. Why did the computer came back home very late?

39. You can catch it but not necessarily with your hands, what is it?

40. If there ever was a spelling competition, what animal would win?

41. An alligator that wears a vest will be called?

42. Why is the white house always clean and spotless?

43. Why do birds fly when going to school?

44. I am tall in the morning, short in the afternoon and I disappear in the night only to reappear soon, what am I?

45. Why are rivers very rich?

46. Why did the cook go to jail?

47. Why did the student had a scissors in his bag?

48. What is fastest way to make a goldfish old?

49. Why is 3+4=6 like your left arm?

50. Which wolf got lost in the jungle?

PRO LEVEL SOLUTIONS

1. An eagle, because it is bald.

2. Because it was stuck in a crack.

3. Ears.

4. Your laps.

5. Running out of gas.

6. Because he is an undercover cop.

7. O I C U (Oh, I see you).

8. Dead.

9. The stone gets wet.

10. Third place.

11. The fence.

12. Two. Inside and outside.

13. None, the ark was Noah's.

14. Microchips.

15. Number 9.

16. Notes.

17. The rail track.

18. A superzero.

19. Because he lost all his patients.

20. You open the refrigerator and put the lion in and close the door of the refrigerator.

21. You open the refrigerator, take out the lion and put the crocodile in, then close the door of the refrigerator.

22. It was the crocodile and it was because it was in the refrigerator.

23. All the wild animals that stays in the stream were at the meeting and the crocodile was in the fridge too.

24. Stop imagining.

25. A blackboard.

26. Hot. Anyone can catch cold.

27. An airplane.

28. It always have too much problems to solve.

29. I am EGGhausted.

30. One of them was bald.

31. Reality.

32. Check the third word in the question.

33. Footsteps.

34. Because he wanted to know how long he slept.

35. Just one. For example, January 2nd, February 2nd.

36. New Jersey.

37. March.

38. He had a hard drive.

39. Cold.

40. A bee.

41. An investiGATOR.

42. Because it lives in WASHINGton.

43. Because they go to high school.

44. The shadow.

45. Because they have banks in them.

46. Because he beat the eggs and battered the fishes.

47. Because he wanted to cut class.

48. Take away the 'g'.

49. Because it is not right.

50. The WHEREwolf.

EXPERT LEVEL

Welcome to the expert level of your favorites riddles and jokes. How many did you get right on the pro level? Let proceed with the final stage.

1. What do you to stop an astronaut's kid from crying?

2. At what point does a joke becomes a 'dad' joke?

3. What would the limestone say to the geologist?

4. What did the watermelon say to the goat?

5. What is the best way to making sure an octopus laughs?

6. Where does the word does comes before start?

7. What common tool do you need for maths classes?

8. What did the teacher with the cross eye say to the principal?

9. I am at the beginning of eternity and the end of time, I am at the beginning of every end possible and the end of every place, what am I?

10. What kind of moth is the biggest?

11. What do you give a lemon that is ill?

12. The older I go, the smaller I become, what am I?

13. I am a country and I am the slipperiest of them all, what country am I?

14. What kind of bird is capable of writing?

15. What runs without legs?

16. Where do elephants keep their valuables?

17. What suddenly becomes bigger when it is upside down?

18. What would you call a beautiful door?

19. How many letters does the alphabet has?

20. Where does the sheep get its haircut?

21. Why did the cat sleep near the computer?

22. What did the mother bee said to her naughty kid?

23. What has no finger but has a ring?

24. How do you get a cool music?

25. Why is the letter 'B' such a cool one?

26. There is a kinda bet that can never be won, what bet is that?

27. What would a paint give the wall on their anniversary?

28. If a cat has a remote, what would be its favourite button?

29. What day has day in but is not Monday, Tuesday, Sunday, Wednesday, Friday, Thursday, and Sunday?

30. What do you always need to break before you use it?

31. Why don't they take tests in zoos?

32. It has words but never speaks, what is it?

33. One day, I was walking by the road but was unfortunately hit by a car that was over speeding so I died. Then I got to heaven and I was happy to see my grandma having a conversation with Adam and Eve, how did I know it was Adam and Eve I saw her with?

34. Where did oak trees originate from?

35. What comes twice in a week, once in a year and never in a month?

36. Did you hear the joke about the bed?

37. What three letter words becomes bigger when you another three letters?

38. What did the cactus say to the porcupine?

39. What did the porcupine say to the cactus?

40. What kind of the year is the frog's favourite?

41. What did the telephone do when he was proposing to his lover?

42. Where in the world can you find the best rope?

43. Airplanes and clothes have one certain thing in common, what is it?

44. What never walks but runs?

45. What stands in the middle of the ocean?

46. A certain letter of the alphabet is an insect, which is it?

47. What letter is a part of the head?

48. Why is letter 'U' the happiest letter of them all?

49. What is capable of filling up a room despite taking no space?

50. When does 11+4=3?

EXPERT RIDDLE SOLUTIONS

1. You rock-et.

2. When the punchline becomes a-pparent.

3. Don't take me for granite.

4. Nothing. Watermelons can't talk.

5. with ten-tickles.

6. in the dictionary.

7. The multi-PLIERS.

8. I am unable to control my

pupils.

9. The letter 'E'

10. The mammoth.

11. A lemon-aid.

12. A pencil.

13. Greece.

14. The PEN-guin.

15. The nose.

16. in their trunks.

17. Number '6'.

18. aDOOR-able.

19. Just 11 letters. T-H-E-A-L-P-H-A-B-E-T-S.

20. At the bah bah shop.

21. So he could keep an eye on the mouse.

22. bee-hive (behave) yourself.

23. The telephone.

24. By putting the radio in the fridge.

25. Because it is between 'A' and 'C' (air conditioner).

26. The alphabet.

27. A new coat.

28. The paws.

29. Today.

30. An egg.

31. There are too many cheetahs.

32. The book.

33. They both had no belly buttons.

34. OAK-lahoma.

35. The letter 'E'.

36. It has not been made yet.

37. Big.

38. Nothing. Cactus can't talk.

39. Are we by any means related.

40. The leap year.

41. He gave her a ring.#

42. in euROPE.

43. The hanger.

44. Water.

45. The letter 'E'.

46. B. (bee).

47. I. (eye).

48. Because it is always in the middle of fun.

49. Light.

50. on the clock.

CONCLUSION

Above are two hundred witty, educative, funny, interesting, intellectual and suitable riddles and jokes for the pleasure of your kids. The answers are intentionally separated from the riddles and jokes questions so it can be more interesting and kids will think deep and take it as a challenge instead of checking the answer instantly after a lazy attempt or out of curiosity. This was done to improve their critical thinking skills, decision making and their problem solving abilities. I hope you enjoy exploring this properly prepared book for the delight of your kids and the whole family.

From the Author

Thank you for buying our riddles and jokes book, we sincerely hope you have enjoyed it!

Can we ask for a small favor? A lot of work goes in to preparing and publishing our books and honest reviews really do help us, especially when it comes to understanding what we should improve in our books.

If you have a minute, we would really appreciate if you could just leave a review...we do actually read our reviews!

Thank you!

Bridget Puzzle Books

Made in the USA
Monee, IL
06 December 2020

51102371R10053